Counting

68 69 [ ] 71 [ ] [ ] 74

sixty-nine   eighty-one

seventy-three

[ ]

77   76   seventy-nine

80 [ ] 82 [ ]

85

eighty-five

eighty

89 88

eighty-eight

ninety-two   [ ]   92 [ ] 94 95

Take a handful of beads. Guess how many. Count and write the number.

Fill in the missing numbers. Match the names to numbers.

Find numbers with 10 letters.

3

Counting in 10s

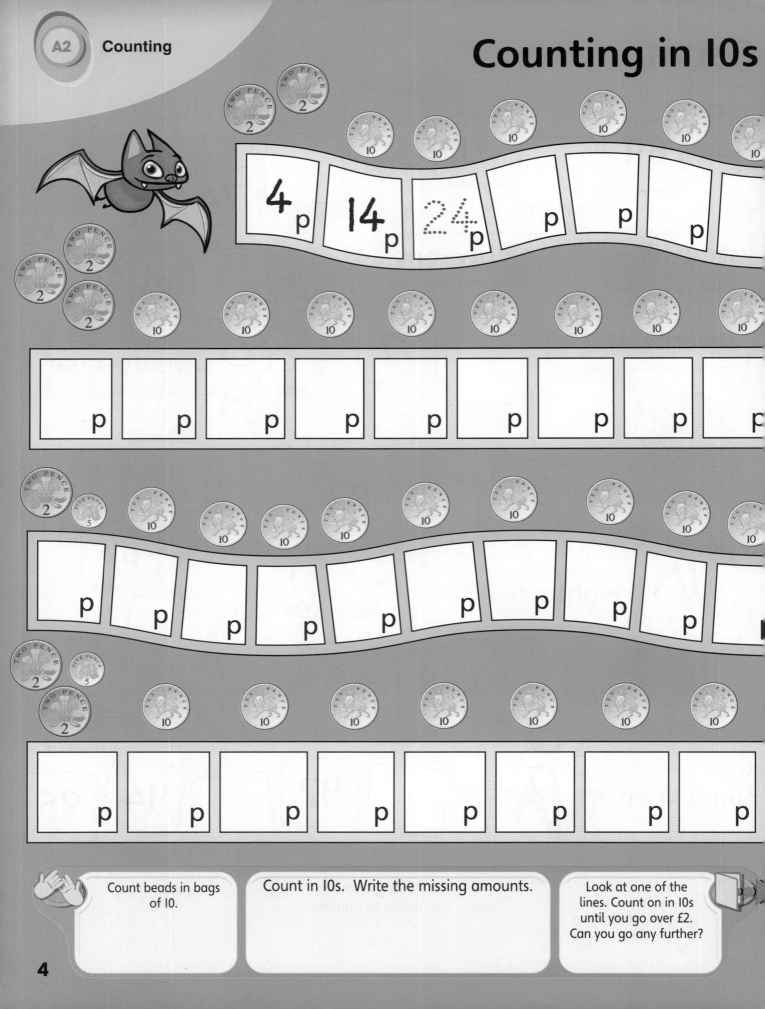

4p 14p 24p ___p ___p ___p

___p ___p ___p ___p ___p ___p ___p ___p ___p

___p ___p ___p ___p ___p ___p ___p ___p

___p ___p ___p ___p ___p ___p ___p ___p

Count beads in bags of 10.

Count in 10s. Write the missing amounts.

Look at one of the lines. Count on in 10s until you go over £2. Can you go any further?

Workbook 2

Framework Edition

Ginn
Part of Pearson

Counting

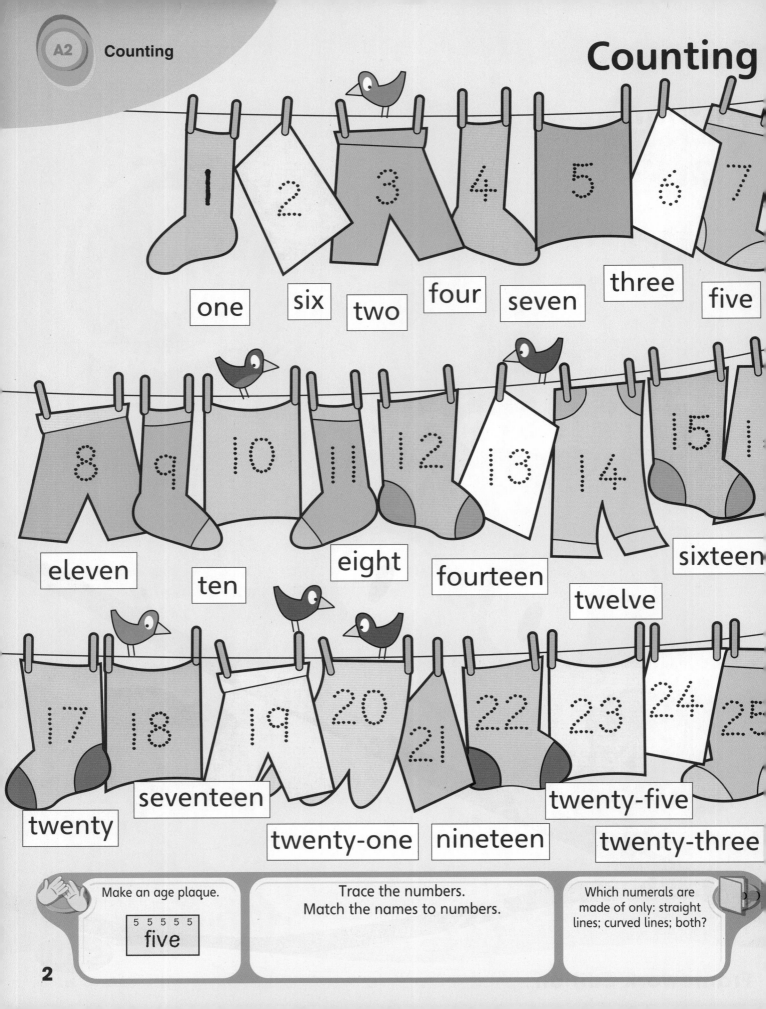

one six two four seven three five

8 9 10 11 12 13 14 15

eleven ten eight fourteen sixteen twelve

17 18 19 20 21 22 23 24 25

twenty seventeen twenty-one nineteen twenty-five twenty-three

Make an age plaque.

5 5 5 5 5
five

Trace the numbers.
Match the names to numbers.

Which numerals are made of only: straight lines; curved lines; both?

Counting in 10s

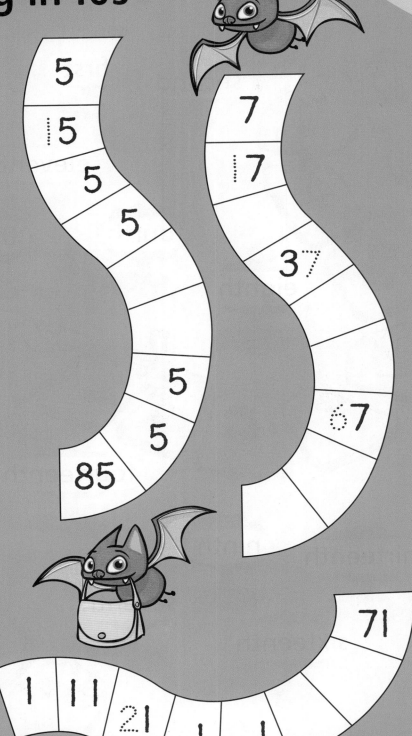

2	12	22	2	2	2	2	2	2	2

5	15	5	5			5	5	85

7	17		37				67		

9	19			49				89

1	11	21	1	1				71

In pairs, choose a 1-digit number. Count on in 10s, taking turns to say each number.

Count in 10s to complete the numbers in each strip.

Start with a 3-digit number, for example 246. Count on in 10s, writing the numbers.

Ordinal numbers

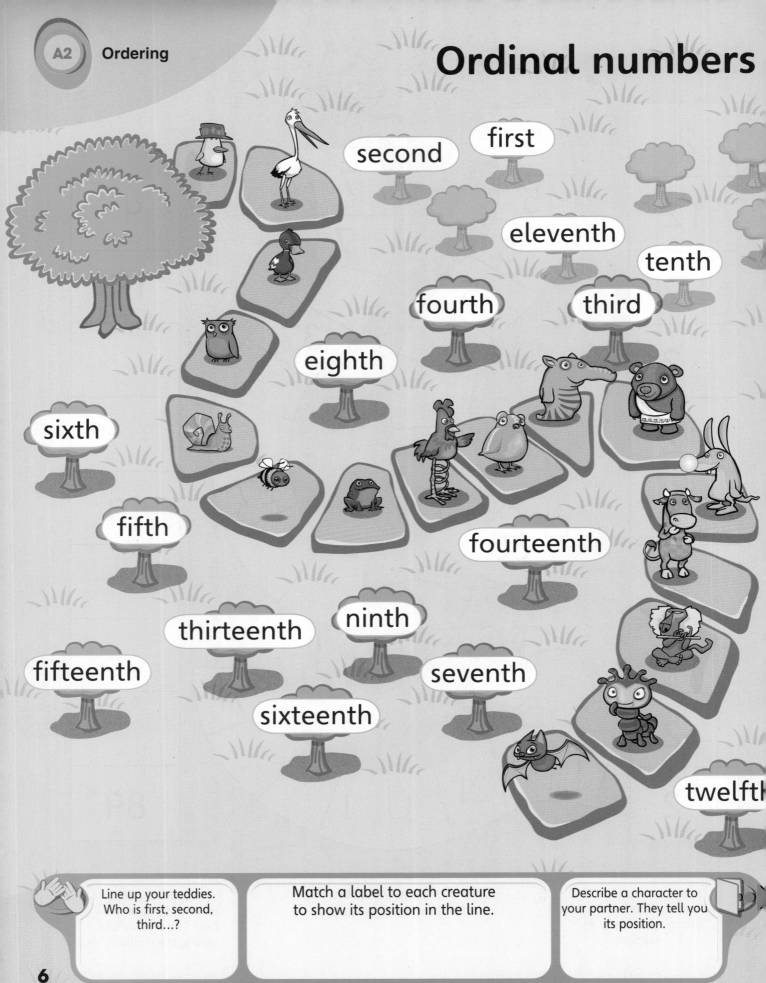

second

first

eleventh

tenth

fourth

third

eighth

sixth

fifth

fourteenth

thirteenth

ninth

seventh

fifteenth

sixteenth

twelfth

Line up your teddies. Who is first, second, third...?

Match a label to each creature to show its position in the line.

Describe a character to your partner. They tell you its position.

Ordinal numbers

First car is **red**

Second car is **not red**

Third car has **stripes**

Fifth and **sixth** cars are **not the same** colour

Fourth car is **blue**

Sixth car is **pink**

Eighth car is **the same** as the **tenth**

Seventh car is **green**

Tenth car has **spots**

Eleventh and **first** cars are the **same**

Ninth and **twelfth** cars are **not blue**

 Line up toy cars in a race. Write labels: first, second…

Colour the cars in the race, looking at the signs!

Make up a race with your own clues.

Comparing numbers

 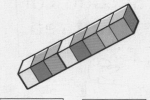 

| 5 | 6 | 7 | 8 | 9 | | | |

 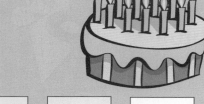  

| 8 | | | | 7 | | | |

| 6 | | | 17 | | | |

| 10 | | | 3 | | | |

| Pick two number cards. Make cube towers for all the numbers in between. | Count and write how many in each set. Write the numbers in between. | Find pairs of numbers with exactly five numbers in between. |

Comparing numbers

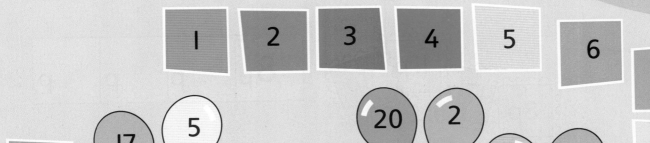

Build Lego models. Compare the number of bricks used.

Cross the balloon with the larger number to pop it!

Investigate which numbers between 30 and 50 can be reversed to make a larger number.

9

Ordering numbers

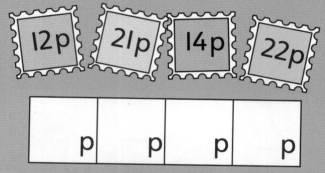

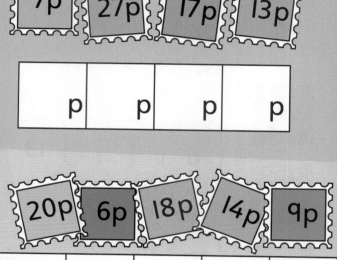

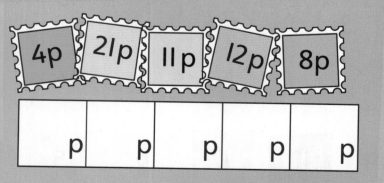

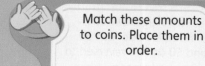
Match these amounts to coins. Place them in order.

Sort each set of prices. Write them in order of size.

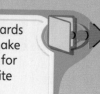
Use the number cards 7, 2, 4 and 3 to make 2-digit numbers, for example 42. Write them in order.

Addition facts

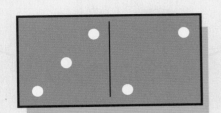

5 + 1 = 6

4 + 1 = 5

3 + 2 = 5

6 + 0 = 6

5 + 0 = 5

4 + 2 = 6

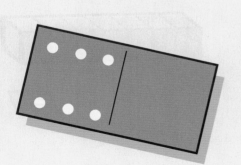

3 + 3 = 6

 Find pairs of playing cards that make 6.

Loop the dominoes that add to 5.
Cross the dominoes that add to 6.
Match each addition to a domino.

How many dominoes have 4 dots? 5 dots? 6 dots? Look for patterns.

Addition facts

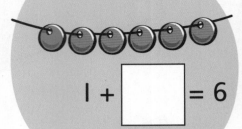

1 + ☐ = 6

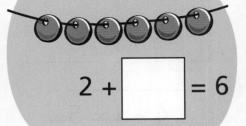

2 + ☐ = 6

3 + ☐ = 6

4 + ☐ = 6

5 + ☐ = 6

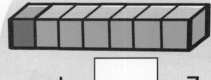

1 + ☐ = 7

2 + ☐ = 7

3 + ☐ = 7

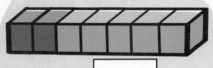

4 + ☐ = 7

5 + ☐ = 7

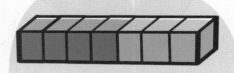

6 + ☐ = 7

Use two colours to make flowers with six petals. How many are different?

Complete the matching additions.

How many ways can you split seven beads into three sets?

Addition facts

6 – 1 = ☐

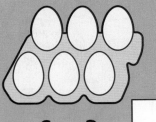

6 – 3 = ☐

6 – 4 = ☐

6 – 2 = ☐

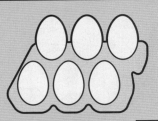

6 – 5 = ☐

7 – 2 = ☐

7 – 6 = ☐

7 – 3 = ☐

7 – 5 = ☐

7 – 1 = ☐

7 – 4 = ☐

Make Plasticine eggs. Squash some! Write the matching subtraction.

Cross the eggs to crack them and complete the subtractions!

Give subtraction clues for your partner to guess, for example: 'My number take away 2 leaves 4.'

Addition pairs

$1 + \boxed{} = 8$

$2 + \boxed{} = 8$

$3 + \boxed{} = 8$

$4 + \boxed{} = 8$

$5 + \boxed{} = 8$

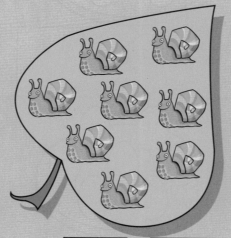

$6 + \boxed{} = 8$

$7 + \boxed{} = 8$

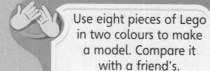 Use eight pieces of Lego in two colours to make a model. Compare it with a friend's.

Draw a line to partition each set of 8. Write the matching addition.

How many different ways can you make 8p?

Subtraction

$8 - 1 =$ ☐

$8 - 3 =$ ☐

$8 - 6 =$ ☐

$8 - 2 =$ ☐

$8 - 7 =$ ☐

$8 - 5 =$ ☐

$8 - 4 =$ ☐

 Make 8 playdough biscuits. Feed some to teddy! Write the subtraction.

Cross buttons in each set to match the subtraction. Complete the subtraction.

Three children's ages add up to 8. How old could they each be?

Addition facts

+	1	2	3	4
1	2			5
2		4		
3				
4		6		

5 + ☐ = 6   5 + ☐ = 7

5 + ☐ = 8   5 + ☐ = 9

 Cover the grid numbers with counters. Take turns to choose a counter, say the number and remove.

Complete the table and the additions.

Write additions with the answer 8, for example: 4 + 4 = 8; 1 + 2 + 2 + 3 = 8...

Above, below, beside, left, right

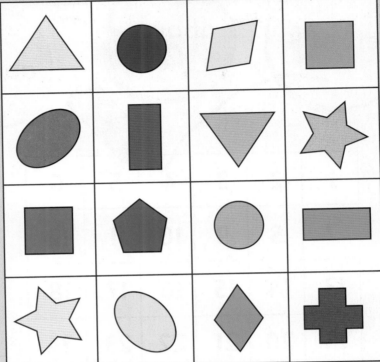

beside

above

left of

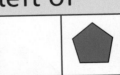

below

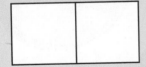

below

right of

beside

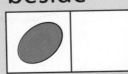

above

 Build a tower of three coloured bricks. What is in the middle? Above? Below? Repeat.

Draw and colour shapes to match the descriptions.

Build a Lego wall in many colours. Give positional clues to identify one brick.

17

Above, below, beside, left, right

left of 5

above 14

above 9

above 21

left of 18

below 13

below 6

below 20

above 30

left of 35

right of 32

right of 22

1	2	3	4	5	6
7	8	9	10	11	12
13	14	15	16	17	18
19	20	21	22	23	24
25	26	27	28	29	30
31	32	33	34	35	36

Put teddy in a box. Place toys above, below, to the left and to the right.

Join each statement to the matching number.

Work in pairs to design a grid. Give clues to place objects in it.

Forwards and backwards

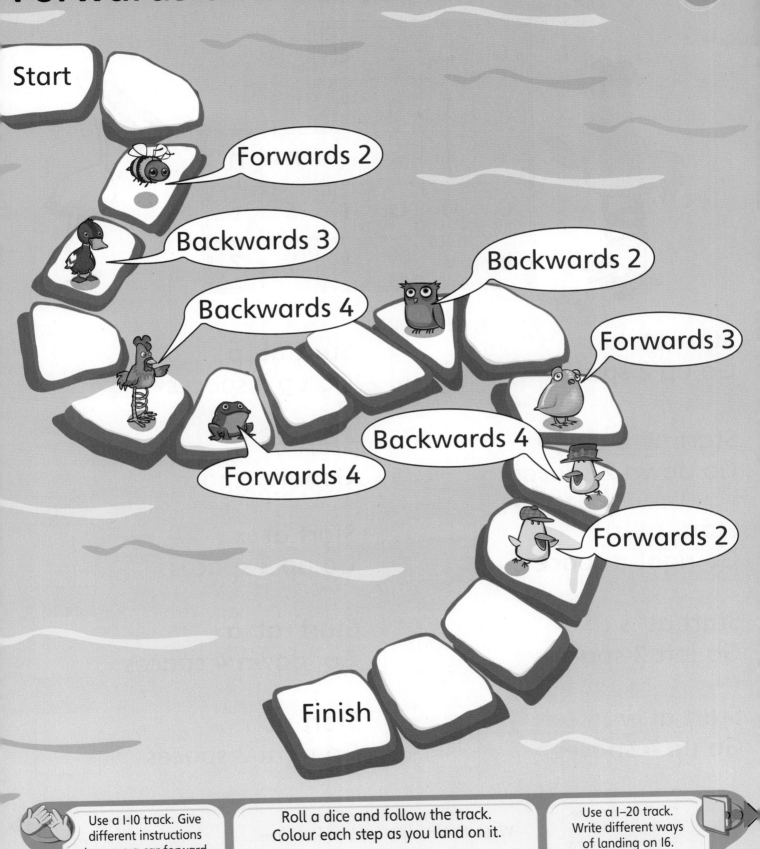

Start

Forwards 2

Backwards 3

Backwards 2

Backwards 4

Forwards 3

Backwards 4

Forwards 4

Forwards 2

Finish

Use a 1-10 track. Give different instructions to move a car forward and back.

Roll a dice and follow the track. Colour each step as you land on it.

Dice.

Use a 1-20 track. Write different ways of landing on 16.

Up, down, left, right

a	b	c	d		
e	f	g	h		
i	j	k	l	m	n
o	p	q	r	s	t
u	v	w	x	y	z

Start at k.
Go up 2 spaces

Start at p.
Go up 3 spaces

Start at d.
Go down 2 spaces

Start at b.
Go left 1 space

Start at u.
Go right 4 spaces

Start at x.
Go up 3 spaces

Start at s.
Go left 2 spaces

Start at a.
Go down 4 spaces

Start at v.
Go up 4 spaces

Start at r.
Go right 2 spaces

Use nine letters to make a grid. Give instructions to move round it.

Follow the instructions.
Write the letter you land on each time.

Describe different routes between your initial letters.

Heavier and lighter

Find two objects of your own: one heavy and one light.

Find each pair of objects in the classroom. Guess the heavier and circle it. Place on the balances. Tick the heavier.
Objects similar to illustrations; bucket balance.

Find three objects heavier and three objects lighter than a book.

21

How heavy?

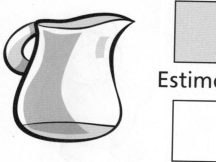

cubes
Estimate

cubes
Actual

cubes

cubes

cubes

cubes

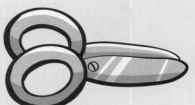

cubes

cubes

cubes

cubes

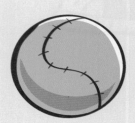

cubes

cubes

cubes

cubes

Place these objects in a line from heaviest to lightest.

Estimate how heavy each object is in cubes. Place on a balance to check.

Objects similar to illustrations; bucket balance.

Choose an object. Find another object that weighs double the number of cubes.

O'clock

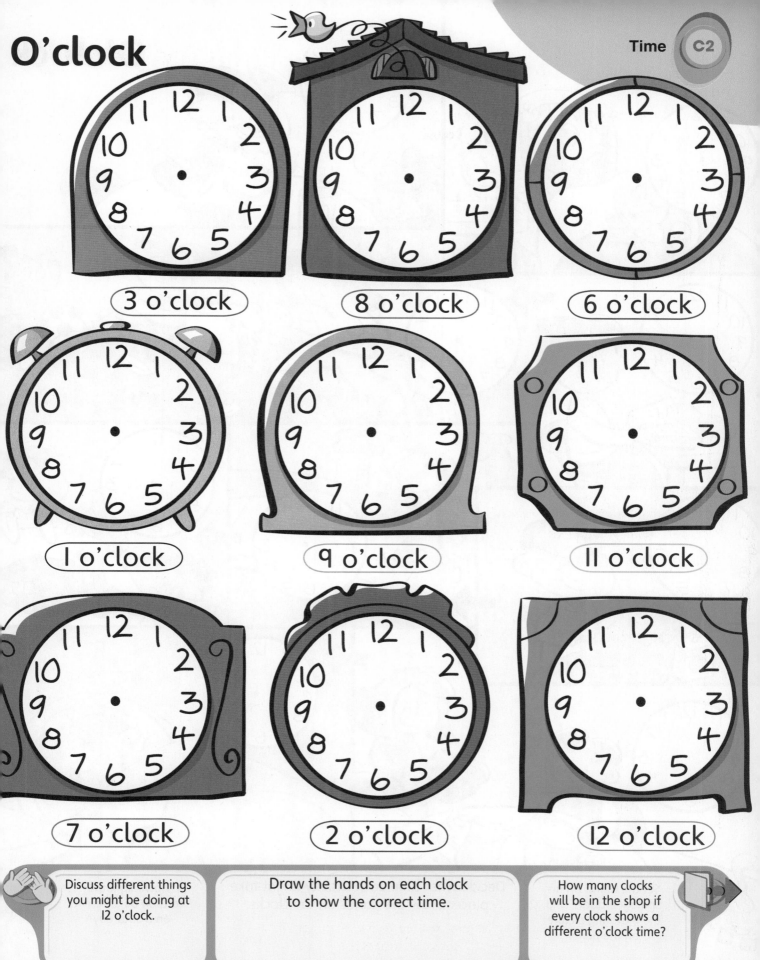

3 o'clock

8 o'clock

6 o'clock

1 o'clock

9 o'clock

11 o'clock

7 o'clock

2 o'clock

12 o'clock

Discuss different things you might be doing at 12 o'clock.

Draw the hands on each clock to show the correct time.

How many clocks will be in the shop if every clock shows a different o'clock time?

O'clock

Set the hands on an analogue clock. Find the matching picture on the page.

Decide what time each activity might take place. Draw the hands on the clocks.

How might the cartoon be different on a Saturday?

Tables

red	
blue	
yellow	

stripey	
spotty	
plain	

Sort red, blue and yellow counters onto the table.

Write how many in each table.

How many spotty red birds are there? Stripey blue birds? Plain yellow birds?

Data

Tables

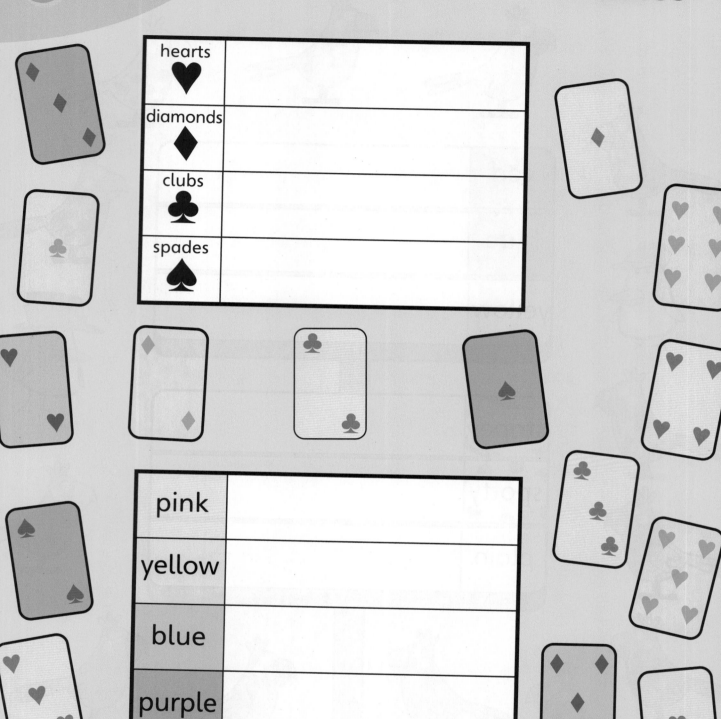

hearts ♥	
diamonds ♦	
clubs ♣	
spades ♠	

pink	
yellow	
blue	
purple	

 Sort playing cards into four suits. How many in each suit?

How many cards are hearts, diamonds, clubs, spades? How many are pink, yellow, blue, purple? Complete the tables.

Create your own set of playing cards with the same number of each type in each set.

3D shapes

pyramids

cubes

cuboids

spheres

| Build a model with cubes and cuboids. | Match each shape to its rocket. | Choose two shapes on the page. How are they the same? How are they different? |

3D shapes

cones

cylinders

Make your own cylinder from card. Fill it with beads.

Draw a loop round all the cones you can see. Cross all the cylinders. Write the numbers of each in the boxes.

Explore how many faces each shape has.

Square faces

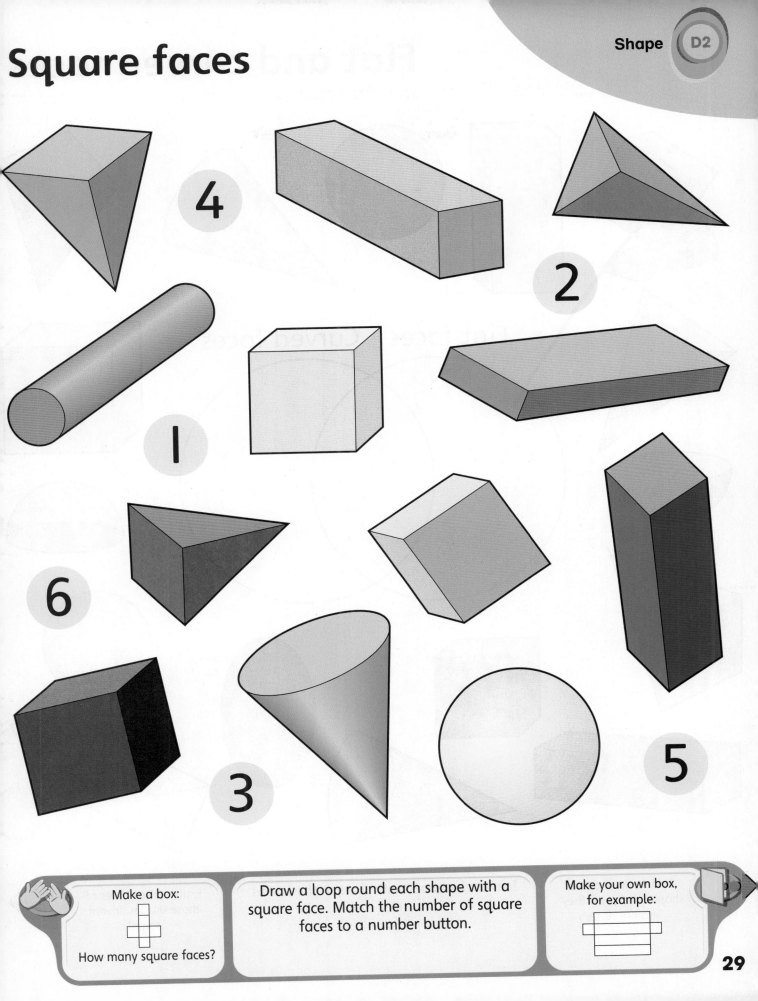

4

2

1

6

3

5

Make a box:

How many square faces?

Draw a loop round each shape with a square face. Match the number of square faces to a number button.

Make your own box, for example:

Flat and curved faces

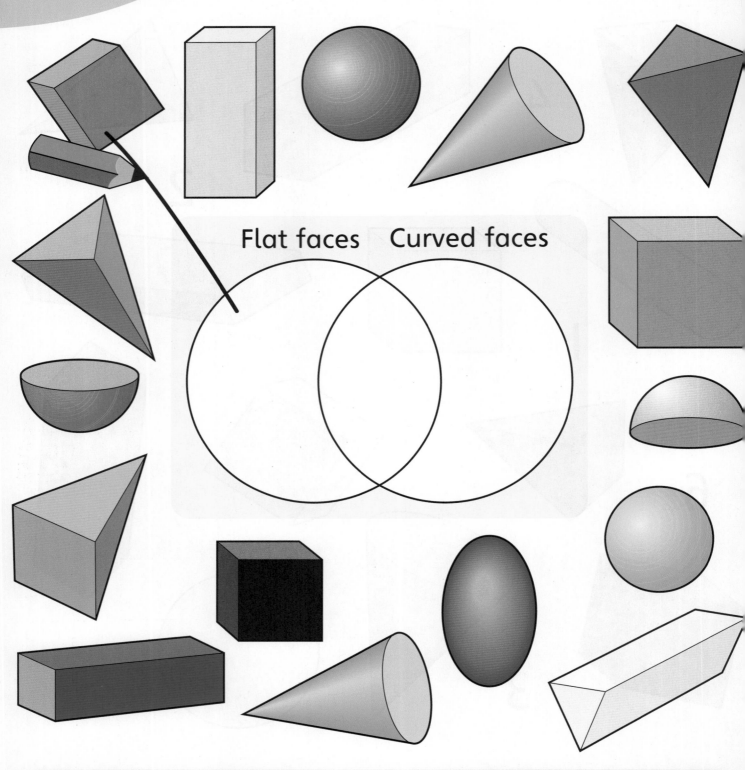

Flat faces   Curved faces

| Find some of these shapes and see if they roll or not. | Join each shape to its place in the hoops. | Explore the names of these shapes. Invent some! |

Counting on

1 2 3 4 5 6 7 8 9 10 11 12 13 14 15 16 17 18 19 20

8 + 3 =

11 + 3 =

13 + 3 =

9 + 4 =

12 + 5 =

16 + 2 =

17 + 3 =

15 + 5 =

Make some dough balls. Write the number. Add some more. Write the total.

Use the number line to help you complete the additions.

How many additions can you write with the answer 20?

31

Counting on

18 + 4 = ☐   18 + 5 = ☐

19 + 3 = ☐   17 + 6 = ☐

17 + 5 = ☐   16 + 5 = ☐

18 + 3 = ☐   19 + 2 = ☐

19 + 4 = ☐   17 + 4 = ☐

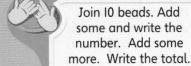 Join 10 beads. Add some and write the number. Add some more. Write the total.

Count up to the wolf and then on. Complete the addition.

Write some additions where you cross other wolf numbers, for example 40.

Adding two numbers

Make a tower of 20 bricks. Add some more and write the total.

Use the number line to help you add the numbers in each pair of flowers. Write the answers on the pots.

Add 4 to 27, 37, 47... Add 5; add 6 and so on. Look for patterns.

How many 10s?

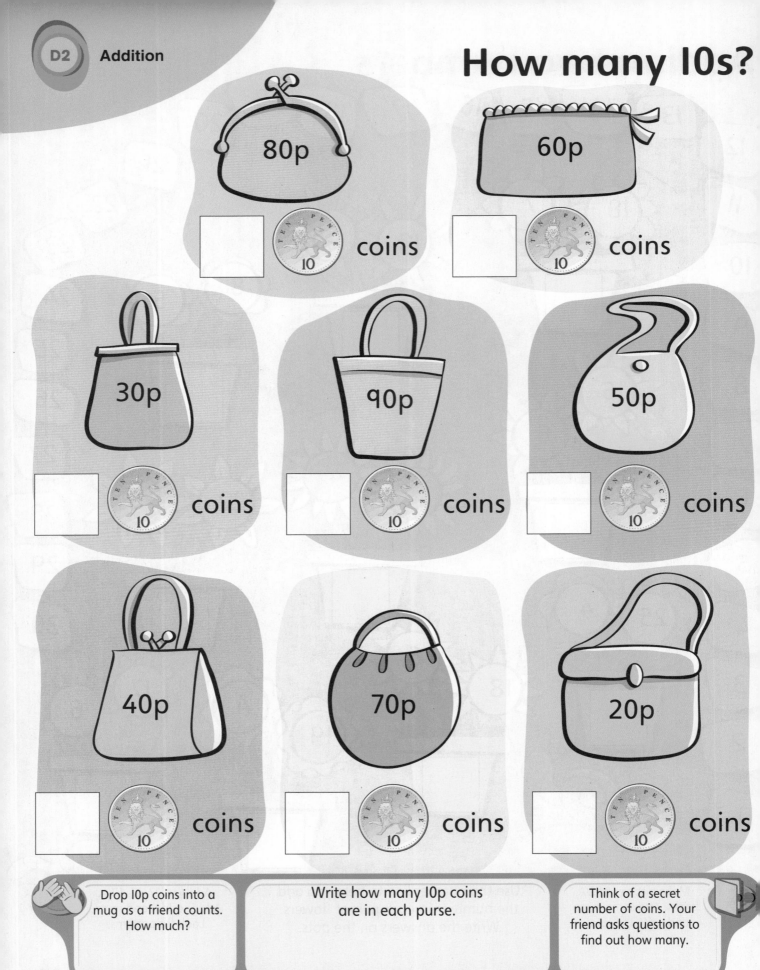

80p ☐ coins

60p ☐ coins

30p ☐ coins

90p ☐ coins

50p ☐ coins

40p ☐ coins

70p ☐ coins

20p ☐ coins

Drop 10p coins into a mug as a friend counts. How much?

Write how many 10p coins are in each purse.

Think of a secret number of coins. Your friend asks questions to find out how many.

Adding 10s

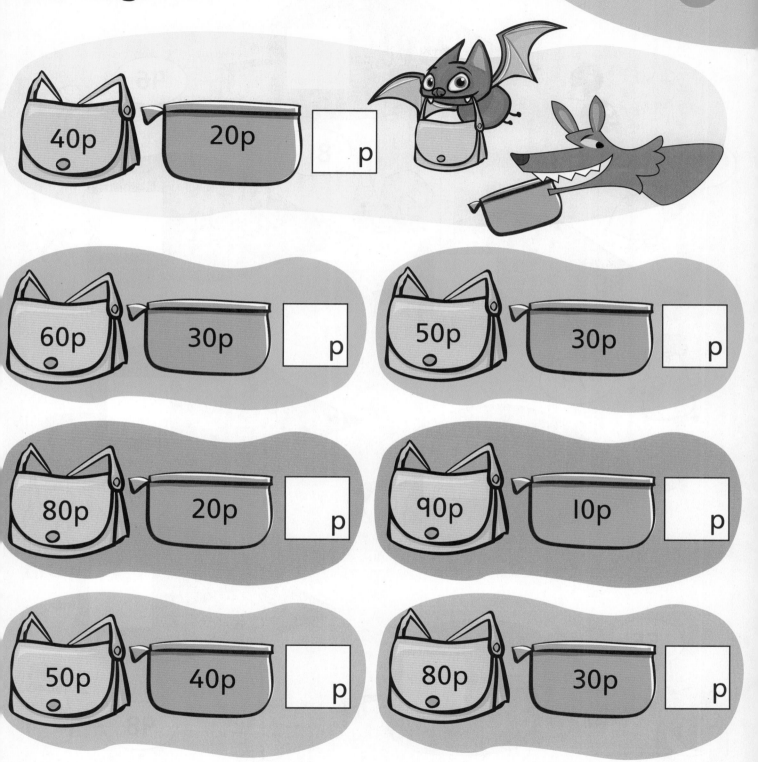

40p | 20p | ___ p

60p | 30p | ___ p

50p | 30p | ___ p

80p | 20p | ___ p

90p | 10p | ___ p

50p | 40p | ___ p

80p | 30p | ___ p

Put 10p coins in two purses. How much altogether?

Add Bisky Bat's and Wolf's pocket money.

How much do you have if you have fifteen 10p coins? Twenty five 10p coins? Thirty five 10p coins?

Adding 10s

42 + 20 = ☐

96

77

81

49 + 30 = ☐

35 + 20 = ☐

79

68 + 30 = ☐

51 + 30 = ☐

62

56 + 40 = ☐

55

37 + 40 = ☐

98

Make 42 with base-10 equipment. Add two more 10s. Repeat with a different number.

Complete the additions. Use the characters to help you.

Choose two numbers, for example 20 and 90. Can you get from one to the other by adding 20s?

Counting in 10s

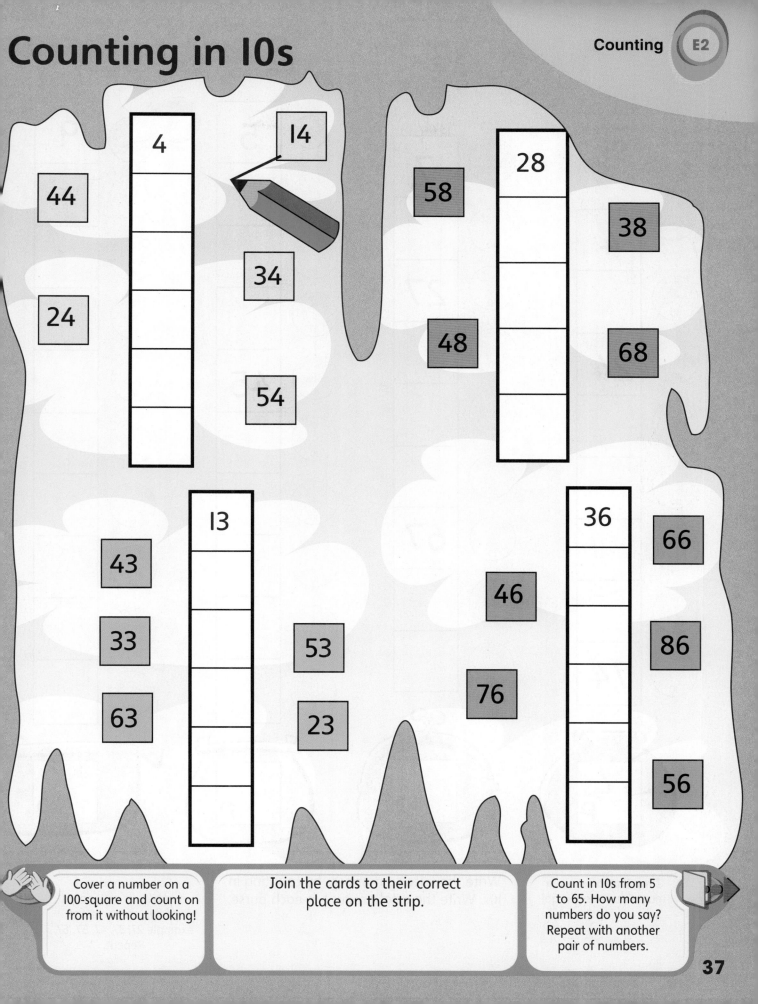

4

14

44

24

34

54

58

28

38

48

68

13

43

33

63

53

23

36

66

46

86

76

56

Cover a number on a 100-square and count on from it without looking!

Join the cards to their correct place on the strip.

Count in 10s from 5 to 65. How many numbers do you say? Repeat with another pair of numbers.

Counting in 10s

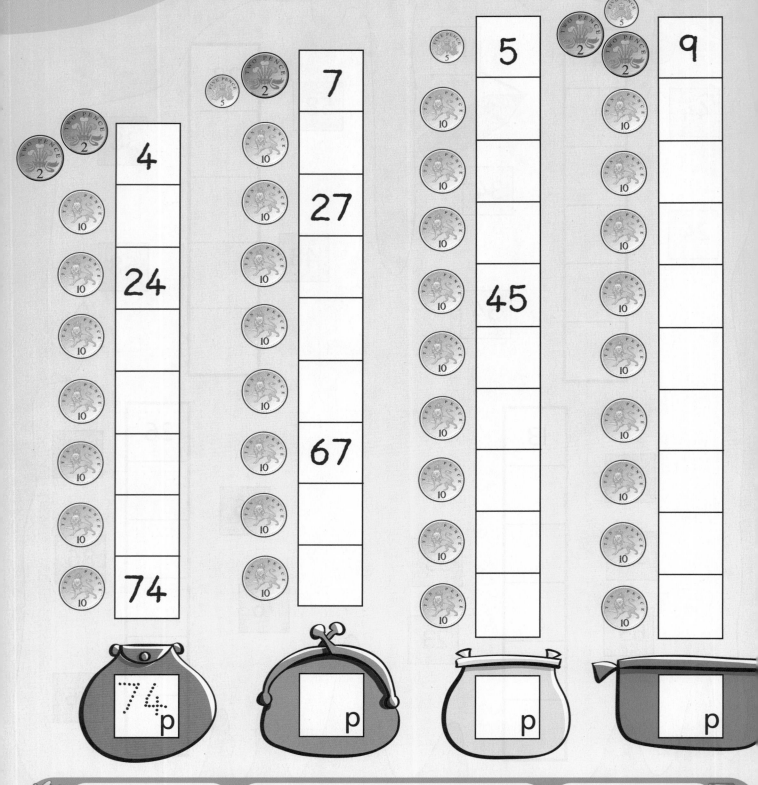

Drop 10p coins into a mug. Count as you go!

Write the missing numbers by counting in 10s. Write the total amount in each purse.

Say start and end numbers in a 10s count of five numbers, for example 27, 37, 47, 57, 67. Repeat.

Counting in 10s

2	3			5	6	7	8		9
12	13		15			17	18		
	23	24	25						
	33	34							
		44				47		49	
			65	66			68		
72		74	75	76	77	78	79		

Draw your own 'counting in 10s' ladders.

Count on or back in 10s to fill in all the ladders in Bisky Bat's cave.

Count in 11s from 3. Look at the pattern on the grid. Repeat with a different start number.

One more, one less

24

85

46

33

72

17

51

69

 Choose a start number, for example 32. Make a track 10 spaces long.

Write the numbers one more and one less.

Choose an animal. Say the numbers two more and two less. Your partner says which animal. Swap.

10 more

 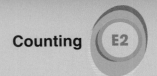

53p ▶ 6̈3̈p

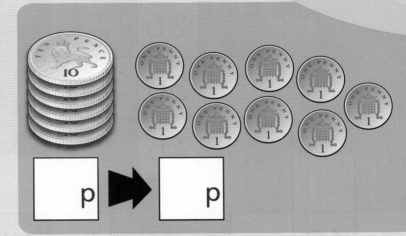

☐ p ▶ ☐ p

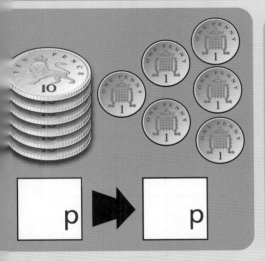

☐ p ▶ ☐ p

☐ p ▶ ☐ p

☐ p ▶ ☐ p

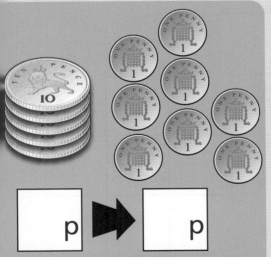

☐ p ▶ ☐ p

☐ p ▶ ☐ p

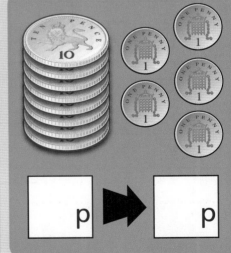

☐ p ▶ ☐ p

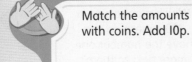 Match the amounts with coins. Add 10p.

Write the amount then write the number that is 10 more.

Using 1p and 10p coins, how many amounts can you make using only six coins?

41

10 more or less

```
        26
    35  36  37
        46
```

```
        28
```

```
    63
```

```
        44
```

```
        12
```

```
        59
```

```
    71
```

```
    87
```

```
        65
```

```
        32
```

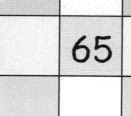

Put some 10p and 1p coins in a purse. How much? Add 10p. How much? Repeat.

Write the numbers one less and one more.
Write the numbers 10 less and 10 more.

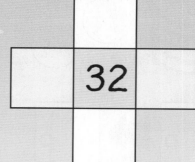

Which numbers on a 100-square do not have the number one more next to them?

Count back in 1s

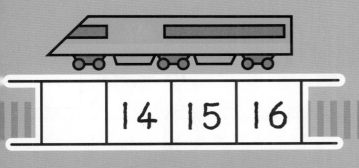

| | 14 | 15 | 16 |

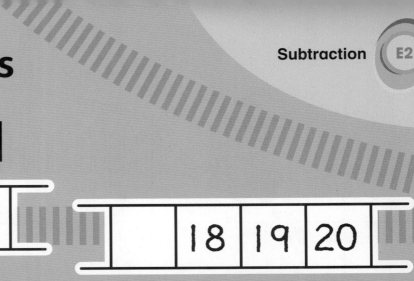

| | 18 | 19 | 20 |

| | 10 | 11 | 12 |

| | 19 | 20 | 21 |

| | 21 | 22 | 23 |

| | 16 | 17 | 18 |

| | 20 | 21 | 22 |

| | 23 | 24 | 25 |

| | 15 | 16 | 17 |

 In pairs, practise counting back, taking turns to say the next number.

Count back one more number and write it in the track.

What is the largest number you can count back from?

Taking away

$16 - 3 =$

$17 - 4 =$

$14 - 3 =$

$18 - 2 =$

$13 - 3 =$

$19 - 4 =$

$15 - 4 =$

Make biscuits.
Give some to teddy.
How many are left?

Cross off the pegs to match the subtraction.
Write the answer.

Write subtractions that
give the answer 15.

Counting back

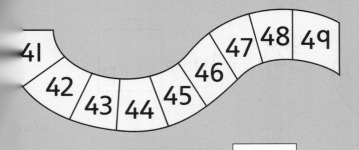

48 – 4 =

46 – 5 =

47 – 3 =

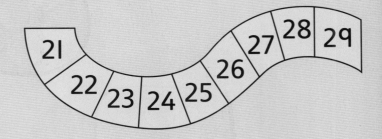

27 – 5 =

25 – 4 =

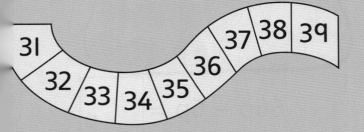

38 – 4 =

35 – 4 =

37 – 5 =

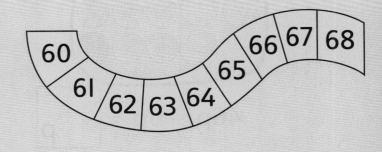

67 – 5 =

66 – 4 =

64 – 4 =

 Make an amount using 10p and 1p coins. Take away the 1p coins. How much is left?

Use the number lines to count back and complete the subtractions.

Explore subtractions that give an answer ending in 0, for example 24 – 4 = 20.

Counting back

34p – 4p = [ ] p

25p – 5p = [ ] p

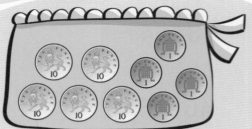

54p – 4p = [ ] p

46p – 6p = [ ] p

66p – 6p = [ ] p

37p – 7p = [ ] p

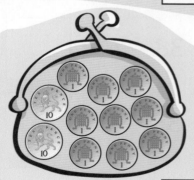

29p – 9p = [ ] p

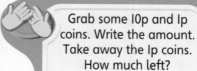

Grab some 10p and 1p coins. Write the amount. Take away the 1p coins. How much left?

Use the purses to do the subtractions.

Explore how much you must take away to leave an amount ending in 9p.

Counting back

24 – 4 = ☐

36 – 6 = ☐

72 – 2 = ☐

29 – 9 = ☐

55 – 5 = ☐

63 – 3 = ☐

37 – 7 = ☐

48 – 8 = ☐

56 – 6 = ☐

68 – 8 = ☐

75 – 5 = ☐

84 – 4 = ☐

 Make the first number with base-10 equipment. Take away the units.

Complete the subtractions.

Other than 6, what numbers can you take away from 76 to leave a number ending in zero?

Talk with your teacher about when to colour an animal.

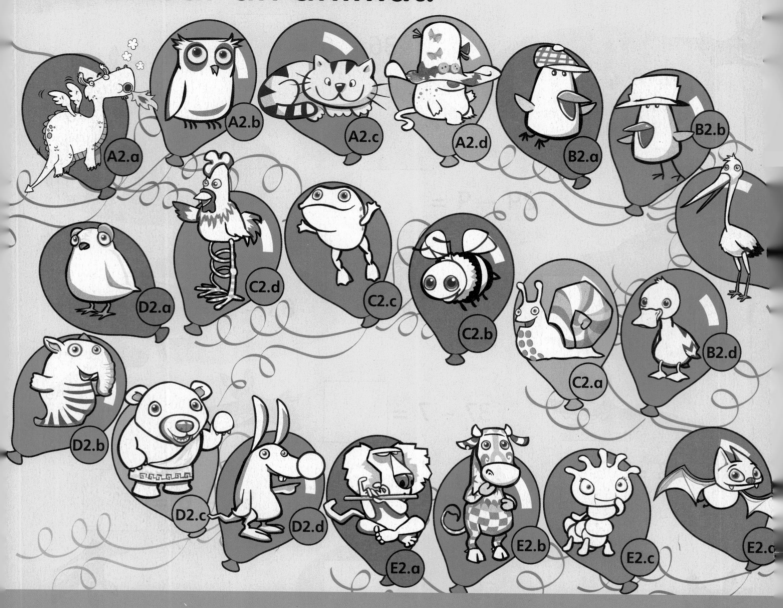

The instructions at the foot of each page are written for teachers to explain to children. The core activity is written in the centre. The activities with the 👏 icon provide a practical activity, often requiring the children to do or make something, while the activities marked with ▱▸ provide an activity for children who require more challenge.

Ginn is an imprint of Pearson Education Limited, a company incorporated in England and Wales, having its registered office at Edinburgh Gate, Harlow, Essex, CM20 2JE. Registered company number: 872828

ISBN: 978 0602 57636 3 © Ginn 2007
First published 2007
Twelfth impression 2012
Printed in Malaysia (CTP-PPSB)

Abacus Evolve Framework Edition

To find out more about Ginn products, plus free supporting resources, visit

www.ginn.co.uk
01865 888020

ISBN 978-0-602576-36-3

Part of Pearson

9 780602 576363